Champion Dog
PRINCE TOM

By **JEAN FRITZ** and **TOM CLUTE**

Illustrated by **ERNEST HART**

SCHOLASTIC BOOK SERVICES

Published by Scholastic Book Services, a division of Scholastic
Magazines, Inc., 33 West 42nd Street, New York 36, N.Y.

2nd printing . . . . . October, 1961

Manufactured in the U.S.A.

To Prince Tom

No dog can become a champion without the help of believing people. Prince Tom has been especially fortunate to have had so much help and encouragement along the way. To all those who have played a part in Prince Tom's life, I am deeply indebted and in particular to the following people, without whose help, Prince Tom would never have had the opportunity to carry out his ideas: to Jim Norris, Gladys Farrand, and Sophia Washburn, Obedience Instructors; to Ginny Wood of WSPD Television Station, Toledo, Ohio; to Dorothy Werch of Adrian, Michigan; to Al Mauder of the Maumee Valley Springer Spaniel Club; to Professional Handlers Bub Knodle and Ruffie Eakin; to Joe Stetson, Dog Editor of FIELD AND STREAM; to Dr. John R. Thompson of Adrian, Michigan, to Miss Joan Tighe of New York City; to Rev. A. H. Wallschlaeger of Owosso, Michigan; and to my mother, Mrs. Elizabeth E. Clute.

Tom Clute

April 18, 1958

B<small>LACK</small> C<small>INDY</small> lay in the corner on her blanket and looked proudly at her new litter of eight little cocker spaniels. Seven of the puppies were as black as tar, as black as Black Cindy herself, as black as their father, Black Satin Chief, and so healthy and strong that any mother would be proud of them. But the eighth puppy wasn't like that at all. He was thin and rather scragglylooking and, because he was a different color, anyone could see right away that he was the smallest of them all, the runt of the litter. He was a blond cocker, the color of butterscotch, and among all the husky black wriggling bodies, he looked like a little sandy mistake.

When Mr. Buell Andrus, Black Cindy's owner, found the puppies, he smiled.

"Good girl, Cindy," he said. "They look just as nice as they always do. Except for the little blond. How did he sneak in there, anyway?"

Black Cindy shook her tail back and forth and

began licking the puppies to show what a good mother she was.

After that, everyone who saw Black Cindy's puppies said the same thing. "Nice little black cockers," they said. "Too bad about the blond one."

Perhaps that was what gave the little blond puppy the idea right from the beginning that he was different. As he grew older, he romped around with his brothers and sisters but, perhaps because he knew he was different, he ran a little faster and jumped a little higher, and played a little harder than the others. But no one noticed that. All anyone noticed was that the little blond puppy was too small.

As soon as the puppies were old enough to leave Black Cindy, Mr. Andrus called up the newspaper in Adrian, Michigan, where he lived. He asked the newspaper to run an advertisement of cocker spaniels for sale. People who were looking for a pet began going out to Mr. Andrus' house to look over Black Cindy's litter.

The puppies were inside a wire pen now in the back yard. Whenever anyone came to see them, they would run around the fence and bark their little puppy barks. The blond puppy barked the loudest and ran the fastest but no one paid any attention. "What nice black puppies," everyone said. Then Mr. Andrus would bring the black puppies out of the pen so that people could see each one more closely. He showed the people what long ears the black puppies had and what fine coats of fur.

"All the black ones will be good-looking dogs," Mr. Andrus said. "We've never tried to raise champions here, but we've raised some mighty fine house pets. Of course they're all purebred cockers."

One by one the black puppies were sold until all that were left in the pen were one black puppy and, of course, the blond one that was too small and too thin for anyone to want.

"Bet we never do get rid of that blond," Mr. Andrus thought one day as he gave the two puppies their food in the pen, "but we ought not to have any trouble with the black one. Think I'll run another ad in the Adrian paper and see if we can't get him off our hands over the weekend."

The next day Mr. Andrus' advertisement appeared in the paper.

FOR SALE. Cocker Spaniel puppies. Buell Andrus, Church Street, Fairfield

Not many people noticed the advertisement. It was in small print in the back of the paper, and it came out on a very hot day in August. Most people were too hot to read small print about cocker spaniel puppies. Many of the people in Adrian weren't even home in the afternoon when the paper boy delivered the paper. They had gone swimming or they were away on vacation. Other people sat in their rocking chairs on their front porches and, when the paper boy gave them the paper, they didn't even read the headlines. They just folded the paper into a convenient size and used it as a fan.

When the paper boy came to the little gray house next to the railroad tracks on Dennis Street, he found Tom Clute sitting on his porch, his shirt sleeves rolled up and his long legs propped on the railing.

"Toss it here, son," Tom called to the boy as he started up the path. Tom caught the paper and, as the boy went on to the next house, Tom opened the paper and began to read. He planned to read only the front page because he had some errands to do before supper. Tom was a jukebox owner and serviceman in

4

and around Adrian. His work often took him out in the late afternoon and evening, but today was so hot, it was hard to get started. Tom read the headlines on the front page and the weather report in the upper right-hand corner and then, instead of putting the paper down as he had meant to do, he turned the page. He read that page and the next page and he kept on reading until he came to the last page. He even read the advertisements. "For Sale," he read, "Cocker Spaniel puppies . . ."

Tom let the paper fall to the floor and he looked dreamily out into Dennis Street. "That's what I'd like," he thought. "A dog." He imagined how it would be if he had one of those cocker spaniels now. He could take the little cocker along to work with him. He would whistle and the dog would jump into the car, and between stops at the restaurants where his juke-boxes were, he would talk to the dog. He might even teach him some tricks. Then later when Tom came home, the dog would be company for him. Of course, his mother was visiting him now from Jackson, but usually he lived alone. A dog would certainly be good company.

Tom chuckled at himself. Here he was a grown man, he thought, and he was still thinking about dogs the same way he had when he was a boy. He'd only had one dog then, a funny little brown dog he had called Prince, and how he had loved him! He remembered how he used to think that someday Prince was going to become famous like Rin Tin Tin. Maybe he would save someone from drowning, Tom had thought, or pull someone out of a burning building. Maybe he and Prince would just happen to be passing by a dog show and the judge would stop everything and point at Prince. "Where did that dog come from?" the judge would say. "He should be the winner."

Of course nothing like that had happened. Only in the movies and in the dreams of boys do things like that happen, and Tom smiled to remember his own dreams. Then he swung his long legs to the floor and got up to go to work.

First he went into the house to say good-by to his mother. He found her in the kitchen, cutting up apples for a pie. Tom reached over and stole a piece of sliced apple and leaned against the kitchen doorway while he ate it.

"Say, Mom," he said. "Remember that crazy little brown dog I had when I was a kid?"

Tom's mother looked up from the apple she was paring. "I certainly do remember Prince. Whatever made you think of him?"

Tom shrugged. "I don't know. Something I saw in the paper, I guess. An advertisement of cocker spaniels for sale."

After Tom had gone to work, his mother went on with her pie. She rolled the bottom crust out and put the apples on top of it and sprinkled sugar on them. She rolled the top crust out and spread it over the apples, but all the time she was thinking.

"A dog might be nice for Tom," she thought. She took a fork and pressed around the edge of the pie to give the crust a ruffle. Tomorrow would be Tom's birthday. A dog might be just the thing. Some friends were planning a surprise party here at his house. Maybe they would like to know about that advertisement in the paper. Tom's mother cut a half-moon in the middle of her pie, and put it in the oven. Then she went to the telephone.

THE NEXT day Tom worked all day, and it was a lucky thing that he did. He didn't go near Dennis Street, so he didn't see his mother spread and swirl white icing over the top and sides of a big birthday cake. He didn't go near Fairfield, where Buell Andrus lived, so he didn't see his friend Ann standing in the back yard looking into a wire pen.

"I want a puppy to give as a birthday present," Ann said.

Mr. Andrus went into the pen and brought out the black puppy. He pulled the puppy's ears down to his nose to show how long they were. Then he set him down on the ground. The little black puppy looked carefully around him at the strangeness outside his pen. He took a cautious step forward, then he looked around again.

"He's a nice-looking dog," Mr. Andrus said. "Big for his age, too. You can have him for fifty dollars."

Inside the wire pen the little blond puppy was racing dizzily around and around. He poked his nose through the wire fence; he stood on his hind legs and he barked, although the sound wasn't exactly a bark. He made a funny little up-and-down noise in his throat that sounded as if he were trying to talk and as if he had a great deal to say.

Ann looked over at the little blond cocker and laughed. "Why don't you bring him out?" she said.

"You want to see the little blond?" Mr. Andrus asked. "You don't know much about dogs, do you?" But he went over to the pen and let the blond dog out.

The blond dog didn't stand around carefully for even one minute. He put his nose to the ground where there were all sorts of exciting smells waiting for him. He followed the smells and he followed his nose as fast as he could go, exploring the new world of the back yard. Then he came back to Ann and he talked to her. Up and down in his throat he told her all about the smells and all about himself and maybe, if anyone had been able to understand him, he even told about some of the wonderful plans he had for himself when he grew up. He tried to wag his little stub of a tail but he was too excited to wag just his tail. He wagged and the whole back half of the little blond puppy went from side to side.

Ann smiled. "I think I'd like to take the little blond," she said.

Mr. Andrus shrugged his shoulders. "Well," he said, "it's up to you. If you want him, you can have him cheap. Twenty-five dollars."

Ann paid for the blond puppy and Mr. Andrus put him in a traveling box. Then Ann put the box in her car and went back to Dennis Street to wait for the party to begin.

At six o'clock everything was ready. The table was set for the party. The guests were gathered in the dining room, waiting for Tom, and in Tom's chair was a great, long box tied up in white tissue paper with an enormous green ribbon. If anyone had looked closely, he would have seen that at each end of the box a round hole was cut in the tissue paper where from time to time a damp black nose appeared. But the nose was small and the holes were small and probably no one would notice unless he already knew about them. Anyone else might think the box was a crate of oranges tied up in green ribbon or a case of Coca-Cola.

When Tom pulled up in front of his house in his black and white station wagon, all the guests moved away from the window so they couldn't be seen.

"Sh, sh . . ." they whispered to each other.

Ann leaned down to the long box. "Sh, sh," she whispered into one of the round holes.

The little blond puppy sat inside his dark box and he kept very quiet. He could hear all kinds of new noises and smell all kinds of new smells, and through his little hole he caught round glimpses of things he had never seen before. He didn't know what it all meant, but because it was new and different he was sure it would be fun. He sat up straight and looked through the hole in one end of his box and waited for the fun to begin. Then he turned around and looked through the hole in the other end.

It was very quiet now in the box, the same kind of quiet there was in the middle of the night in Mr. Andrus' pen. No, it wasn't the same kind, either. It wasn't a sleeping quiet; it was an excited quiet. The little blond puppy could feel prickles of excitement going up and down his back. Then he heard a squeaky noise which he found out later was the noise a screen door makes when it opens. A man's big voice called out.

"Hi, Mom! What's for supper?"

Suddenly there was a tremendous noise of voices, as loud as if all the dogs in the world had been turned loose.

"Surprise! Surprise!" the voices said. "Happy Birthday!"

The big voice of the man came close and laughed so happily that the little blond puppy pressed up to his hole to see more. All he could see were hands.

"Open it, Tom," the voices said. "Go ahead and open it!"

The hands made a wonderful crackling sound with the paper around the box and before long the paper was gone. The hands worked at one end of the box. Then that end of the box opened up and there was the face of the man looking in at the little blond puppy and grinning.

"Well, I'll be a monkey's uncle!" the man said. "A little cocker spaniel."

The blond puppy rushed out of his box and onto Tom's lap. He put his front paws on Tom's chest and licked his face. Then he jumped down onto the floor to go after some of those smells he'd been smelling. He ran around the dining room between the legs of chairs and between the legs of people. He went into the living room, which was even more exciting because it was full of fine jumping places — big armchairs, a sofa, a low coffee table on which there were more smells, and each one different. Then he raced into the kitchen, where the smells were most interesting of all. On the floor beside the stove he found a white bowl filled with a delicious kind of eating.

All the time that Tom and his guests were at dinner and later when they were in the living room, the little blond puppy rushed around the house, into every corner he could find, onto every jumping place he could reach. But between jumps he came to Tom and he talked to him, up and down in his throat.

"He looks pretty thin," Tom's mother said.

"Rather small for a cocker, isn't he?" one of the guests asked.

Tom reached down and lifted the little blond puppy onto his lap. He looked at the puppy's eager brown eyes and his little stump tail quivering with excitement.

"He looks great to me," Tom said. "He looks perfect."

"Well, I expect we can fatten him up," Tom's mother said. "I hope so. What are you going to call him, Tom?"

Tom patted the puppy's head and he scratched the exact spot on his chest where all puppies like to be scratched.

"I think I'll call him Prince," Tom said.

3

Tom didn't think when he gave the little blond puppy the name Prince that anything more would ever be added to his name. But "Prince" was only the beginning. Perhaps the little blond puppy knew that. Perhaps he had an idea even then that one day, if he were given a chance, he could have one of the longest names any dog ever had. Perhaps that was what he was trying to tell Tom when he talked up and down in his throat.

Tom took him to see a veterinarian soon after the birthday party and found out that, like many little puppies, Prince had worms. After he had taken medicine, he began to look better and put on weight. He would always be a small dog, the veterinarian said, but Tom didn't care and certainly Prince didn't.

Being small didn't change Prince's ideas about what he could do. Sometimes he would sit on Tom's lap and talk about his ideas in his own up-and-down way.

After a while, when Tom didn't answer, Prince would stretch up and lick Tom's cheek. "It's all right, Tom," he seemed to be saying. "I can understand everything *you* say, but if you can't understand everything *I* say, it's all right. I love you anyway."

Tom had a great many ideas, however, that Prince approved of. He liked the idea of riding with Tom in his black and white station wagon when he went to work. He liked the idea one fall day of going with Tom to see his friend Dr. Thompson, who lived in the country on a big farm.

When the station wagon pulled up beside the farmhouse, Prince bounced up and down with excitement. He could see through the window that he had never been here before and any place that was new was sure to be fun. When Dr. Thompson's five children streamed out of the back door of the farmhouse toward the car, Prince knew the fun had started.

First there was Peter Thompson, then Nathan, Karen, Joey, and Ruth. All of them were shouting at Tom.

"Hi, Tom!" they shouted. "Did you bring your new dog? Let's see your new dog!"

Nathan was the first to reach the car. He looked through the closed window and there was Prince on his hind legs, his front paws on the window sill. Prince looked at Nathan on the other side of the window and he licked the glass between them.

"He's nice," Peter said, looking over Nathan's shoulder.

Nathan grinned. "He sure is."

After Prince had been let out of the car and after he had made friends with each of the children and had settled down for a moment on Nathan's lap, Nathan turned to Tom.

"What's his name?" he asked.

Tom sat down on the back step. "Prince," he said, and as he said it, Prince jumped down from Nathan's lap and ran over to Tom.

"No, no," Tom laughed. "I wasn't calling you. I was just telling Nathan what your name is."

Prince went back to Nathan who, like Tom, seemed to know about the place on a puppy's chest where it's nice to be scratched.

"Prince," Nathan repeated. "What else?"·

Tom laughed. "Nothing else. Just Prince. Isn't that enough?"

Nathan shook his head. "No, it's not enough," he said. "Animals should have at least three names, just like people. All our animals do."

"I'll say they do," Peter agreed. "When Nathan's finished, every chicken has so many names that not even the chicken can remember them."

Nathan looked into Prince's brown eyes. "I bet he'd like some more names," Nathan said. "My turtle's got three names and he likes them."

"What do you call your turtle?" Tom asked.

"Jonner Poky Thompson. And my parakeet's name is Winky Roy Thompson."

"Well, they sound like good names," Tom agreed, "but I think I'll just call my dog Prince. I'd better tie him up now. I'm going in to see your father and I wouldn't want Prince to run off."

After Tom had gone into the house, Prince sat down at the end of the long rope tied to a cherry tree and Nathan sat down beside him.

"You would, too, like some more names, wouldn't you?" Nathan asked and he nuzzled his face into the silky softness of Prince's neck. "I bet you'd like to get off that rope and play with me too." Nathan lay down on his back and put Prince on his stomach. "Not much fun being tied up on an old rope, is it? Nothing to do.

18

Not much to see. I tell you what, Princey." Nathan put Prince on the ground and jumped to his feet. "I'll do some of my tricks and you can watch."

Nathan turned a somersault for Prince. Then he stood on his head. He tried to walk on his hands, but he couldn't do that very well and he fell over in a lump.

Prince sat up straight and began to talk fast and trembly in his throat.

"He likes my tricks," Nathan thought. "I'll do some more." He did a running jump over a rose bush and he turned a backward somersault that came out sideways. By this time Prince was pulling on his line and he was talking very loud. Up and down, up and down.

"Look at Prince," Nathan called to his brother Peter. "Come on and do some tricks with me for Prince."

Peter and Nathan began to play leapfrog, and then Karen joined them, and Joey and Ruth. Four of the children made themselves into huddles on the ground and the fifth one leaped over them, one at a time.

Prince pulled his line tight; then he tugged on it and jerked it and scolded it. He didn't just talk in his throat now; he barked—short, sharp barks that could mean only one thing, "Let me loose. Let me loose."

Nathan went over and put his arms around Prince. "You want to play too, don't you? I'm going in and ask Tom to untie you."

But Nathan didn't need to go in. Both Tom and Dr.

Thompson were stepping out of the door and onto the back porch, and they could see what was going on.

"As long as I'm out here," Tom called to Nathan, "you can untie him."

Prince shook with excitement as he waited for Nathan to let him free. He wagged every part of his body that he could possibly wag and covered Nathan's hands and face with hurry-up kisses. Finally the knot was undone. Prince turned around and looked at the four huddles still on the ground—Peter, Karen, Joey, and Ruth—waiting for Nathan to go on with the game. Then, as if all Prince's life he'd been getting ready for this moment, he raced toward the huddles. He jumped over Peter in one great bounding leap. He hardly hit the ground and he was up again—over Karen, then Joey, then Ruth. When he had finished, he looked ahead of him for more children and when there weren't any, he turned around and began all over again.

Tom stood on the back porch, laughing. "Well, I'll be a monkey's uncle!" he said.

The children rolled over and over on the ground in their excitement. Then they got down in their huddles again and this time Nathan went into a huddle too. "Come on, Prince!" they shouted.

Prince didn't need any encouragement. He sailed over Peter and Nathan and Karen, but when he came to Joey and Ruth, he found they were rather close

together, so he went over both of them in one leap.

"He's some jumper," Dr. Thompson said. Then he called to the children. "Karen, move over close to Ruth and Joey. Let's see how far Prince can jump."

Peter and Nathan stood with Dr. Thompson and Tom while the other three huddled together.

"Come on, Prince," Karen called.

Prince didn't hesitate. He made a flying jump over the three children and landed on the other side with room to spare.

"You get down there too, Peter," Dr. Thompson said.

Prince went over the four children as easily as he had gone over one. Then while they all held their breath, Nathan got down on the ground too.

"He can't do that," Tom said. "Look how small he is."

But Prince couldn't see how small he was. He made a racing start and then he jumped. His legs stretched straight before him and after him in one long golden line and his ears blew up like a rabbit's. He cleared all five children and then, while everyone cheered, he ran to Tom. He pushed his nose into Tom's hands and he talked deep in his throat. "See?" he seemed to say. "This is one of those ideas I was telling you about."

Dr. Thompson nudged Tom. "You've got some dog there, Tom. You know that, don't you?"

"I guess so," Tom grinned. "What do you think of him, Nathan?"

Nathan sat on the ground and his eyes never left Prince. "I think he's the best dog in the world," he said slowly, "*and* I think he needs another name. At least one more name. I think you ought to call him Prince Tom."

Prince wagged his tail and Tom smiled. "All right, Nathan," he said. "We'll call him Prince Tom. I'll send that name in to the American Kennel Club and that's the way we'll register him. Prince Tom. It sounds good."

TOM sent the name in to the American Kennel Club
the next day and several weeks later the registration
certificate came back. It was an official record of
Prince's birth, pedigree, and name. But his name was
no longer just Prince Tom. The certificate had added
something to it.

> Blond Cocker Spaniel
> Date of Birth: March 10, 1950
> Mother: Black Cindy
> Father: Black Satin Chief
> Name: Prince Tom III

Two other Prince Toms were already registered with
the American Kennel Club, a letter explained, so this
Prince Tom had to be registered as Prince Tom III.

"Prince Tom the Third!" Tom repeated. "Won't
Nathan like that!"

Nathan did like it. "I'm glad his name is longer," he said. "Of course, we can still call him Prince or Princey, but now everyone knows that *officially* his name is Prince Tom III." Nathan picked Prince up and held him on his lap. "An animal can't ever have too many parts to his name," he said. "Especially a dog like you, Princey."

Several times a week now Tom was bringing Prince out to Dr. Thompson's to practice his jumping. They soon discovered that Prince could do more than jump. He learned to shake hands and roll over and sit up, but he wasn't much interested in these tricks. As soon as he arrived at the farmhouse, he would go quickly around to all five of the Thompson children and hold out his paw to shake hands. He would roll over and he would sit up on his hind legs, and then he would bounce from one to another and begin to talk. "Now that the baby stuff is over," he seemed to say, "let's get on with the *real* tricks."

His favorite trick was barrel rolling. Tom would bring a barrel from the back of the station wagon and Prince would stand up on his hind legs and roll the barrel across the yard. If Tom didn't bring the barrel out soon enough, Prince would look around for something else to roll. One day he found Karen's doll carriage in the back yard and he stood on his hind legs and wheeled it all round the house. After that, Karen always put her doll carriage out and let her dolls take

turns being pushed by Prince Tom.

During the next months Prince learned to smoke a cigarette, to put matches and candles out, to take off a hat, and to play hide and seek with a ball. He would put his head down between his paws while the children hid the ball, and wouldn't even peek until it was time.

Prince's ball was one of several toys Tom had bought for him. He had a rubber fire plug, a rubber bone, a pipe, a toy mouse, and a dumbbell. Tom kept them all in a special red and white beach pail. He would say to Prince, "Why don't you play with your fire plug for a while, Prince?" And Prince would go to his pail and pick out the fire plug from all his toys. Or Tom would say, "You haven't played with your mouse for a long time." Then Prince would pick out his mouse.

The only trouble was that Prince liked to do his tricks all the time. If he saw a baby carriage on the sidewalk, he wanted to push it. If he saw two boys playing ball, he wanted to join them. If he saw anyone light a match, he wanted to slap it out. If Tom had ever tried to keep a candle lighted in his house, it would have been hopeless with Prince around. When Tom's mother visited, she had a hard time even lighting the oven. She would strike a match and before she could get it to the right spot in the oven, Prince would dash up and put the match out with a quick swipe of his paw. Then he would sit down beside the oven and

27

wait for another match. Finally Tom's mother would have to send Prince out of the room and close the door until the oven was lit.

People all over Adrian began to hear about Prince Tom's tricks. Children rang the doorbell on Dennis Street and asked to see Prince perform. Prince was invited to do his tricks for parties and club meetings, and once his picture was in the paper. The news that Tom Clute had a smart dog spread as far as Toledo.

One day Tom received a letter from Toledo. In the upper left-hand corner of the envelope were the words "WSPD Television Station, Channel 13, Toledo, Ohio." The letter was from Ginny Wood, who conducted a regular television show for children.

"Dear Mr. Clute," the letter said. "We have heard of your dog, Prince Tom III, and we would like very much to have him appear as guest of honor at one of our March shows. If you are willing to come, will you pick a date that is convenient for you in March?"

Tom whistled. "What do you think of that!" he said. He called Prince over and showed him the letter. "You know what, you little rascal?" he said. "You're going to be on TV."

Prince cocked his head to one side. Whatever Tom was talking about must be good because he sounded happy. And if Tom was happy, Prince was happy and he wagged his tail to show it.

Tom read the letter again. Any day in March. "What

about Prince's birthday?" Tom thought. Prince would be a year old on March 10th. Tom would write to Ginny Wood and suggest that Prince come on his birthday.

Tom scratched Prince's chest with his right hand and with his left hand he rubbed him behind the ears.

"On TV," Tom grinned. "Just like Rin Tin Tin."

As soon as Prince Tom woke up on March 10th, he knew this was going to be a special kind of day. He went outside for his morning walk with Tom and he could feel the specialness in the March wind. It was the kind of wind that blows a dog's ears straight back and carries with it all sorts of exciting smells from unknown places. It made Prince want to run and leap over hedges and chase squirrels. On a day like this he might even be able to climb a tree if he tried. He did try and he wasn't able, but it didn't matter. Not on a day like this.

Even Tom acted special today. Instead of going to work, he stayed home and brushed Prince better than he had ever been brushed before. Tom brushed him until the fur on his back glistened and until the fur on his legs, that Tom called his feathers, stood out soft and shiny.

That afternoon Tom called him to go in the station

wagon. Tom wasn't wearing his working clothes; he was wearing his good blue suit and a white shirt and a red tie. They drove out to Dr. Thompson's and that was special, too, because they didn't get out of the car as they usually did. Tom just opened the door and Nathan shoved into the front seat beside Prince and hugged him. "Happy Birthday, Princey," he said. Then the three of them drove off into the March wind and new smells blew into the car and excitement flashed around them like streaks of lightning.

The excitement flashed stronger and stronger all afternoon until Prince found himself in a large room, with Tom and Nathan, and a great many people rushing up and down ladders and swinging enormous lights about. Here the excitement wasn't just flashing; it was crackling like electricity. Prince could feel the crackling in Tom's and Nathan's hands when they touched him; he could hear it in their voices when they talked. "Time now," Tom said. "We'll be going on in a minute."

Then everyone stood still on the ladders and a lady walked into the glare of all the lights and began to talk.

"Today we have with us from Toledo," she said, "seven girls from a local Brownie troop, and from farther away we have from Adrian, Michigan, a special guest of honor who is celebrating his first birthday. Prince Tom the Third."

All at once Prince was in the lights, too, with Tom and the lady and seven girls in Brownie uniforms. In front of him the room was filled with children and they were all clapping. Tom told Prince to shake hands with the lady and with the seven Brownies, and when he did, the children clapped again. It was a wonderful noise that the children made and, no matter what Prince did, the children made the same fine clapping noise.

One of the Brownies went down into a huddle on the floor where the lights were brightest and Tom told Prince to jump over her. The children clapped louder than ever. More and more Brownies got down on the floor until at last all seven were huddled together. For a moment the room was quiet and rather crackly again. Prince had never jumped over that many children before but he wasn't worried. He sprang into the air, stretched straight, and sailed over the seven girls and, just as he had hoped, the room exploded with noise.

Prince had never had so much fun. He rolled his barrel, he wheeled a carriage, he played hide and seek with the Brownies. And always, after everything he did, there was that lovely, thundery clapping.

Then Tom told Prince to get up into a chair and the lady brought a table and placed it in front of Prince. In the center of the table was a big white cake, and in the center of the cake was a white candle. The Brownies stood around the table and sang "Happy

Birthday" while Prince looked at the cake and at the little lighted candle. It was flickering and flickering. Prince knew what to do about flickering. He jumped to the table and with a quick slap of his paw put out the candle. Then he sat down on the table and licked the white sticky frosting from the bottom of his paw and listened to the beautiful noise that was all mixed up with a happy kind of laughing.

It was then that Prince saw the other blond cocker spaniel sitting on another table in front of another birthday cake. No one noticed when Prince stopped licking his paw and began staring at the television set. It was a set like the ones in every television studio, called a monitor, which showed what was being televised at the moment. Prince lifted his nose into the air and sniffed. He couldn't smell another cocker spaniel but he could certainly see one. Everything that he did, the other cocker seemed to do at the same time. All at once Prince jumped over the birthday cake and onto the floor. He ran between the legs of the Brownies and over to the television set. He stood on his hind legs and looked closely at the other blond cocker who stood on *his* hind legs and looked at Prince. Prince licked the television set and the seven Brownies squealed and giggled. The other children in the room broke into the wildest clapping of the afternoon, and the men on the ladders grinned and turned all their cameras on Prince and the television set. Prince began to do his tricks all over again for the other dog, only this time it was even more fun because the other dog did the tricks right along with him. He sat up and the other dog sat up; he rolled over and the other dog rolled over.

But all at once the other dog disappeared and someone said the show was over. Prince ran around the television set, barking and looking for the other dog but he couldn't find him. There was only a blank gray place where the other dog had been. Prince sat down and cocked his head at the blank place, but the dog didn't come back, so Prince looked around for other excitement. There was plenty of that.

The men were coming down from the ladders now. They all laughed and patted Prince and told him what a good dog he was. The seven Brownies crowded around him. "Isn't he sweet?" they said. "Isn't he cute? Isn't he adorable?" Then Nathan, who had watched the show from the side of the stage, pushed through the group of Brownies and knelt down on the floor beside Prince. He lifted up Prince's left ear and he whispered into it. "Princey, I'm so proud, I could bust," he said.

Above Prince and Nathan, Ginny Wood and Tom and the men from the ladders laughed and talked. "It was one of the best shows we've ever had," Ginny Wood said. "Prince Tom is wonderful. Where did he ever learn so much? Has he been to an obedience school?"

Tom laughed. "Prince never went to any school," he said. "I don't think anyone ever taught him much. Prince has usually had the ideas himself and told us about them."

Nathan looked up from behind Prince's ear. He couldn't let this conversation go on without first asking Ginny Wood a question.

"What's an obedience school?" he asked.

"A school where dogs can learn to obey certain commands and pass certain tests," Ginny said. "Afterward, they can go into competition with other dogs."

Nathan's eyes lighted up with more questions. So Ginny Wood went on to explain about the competitions. "They're called Obedience Trials," she said, "and judges give the dogs points for their performance. When a dog wins 170 points or more out of a possible 200 points at three different Obedience Trials, he is given a degree, or title, by the American Kennel Club. He's called a Companion Dog; the initials C.D. follow his name and become a part of his name for always."

"Well, gee," Nathan said, his arms around Prince, "Princey could learn any old commands faster than other dogs, I bet."

"I bet, too," Ginny agreed. "Maybe you'd like to think about that."

There was a lot to think about on the way home. Tom and Nathan and Prince sat quietly in the front seat of the station wagon, going over in their minds the wonderful afternoon. Every once in a while Tom would laugh and take his hand off the wheel and scratch Prince. "You little rascal," he would say.

It was dark now. Nathan stared out happily at the long road unwinding ahead and at the lights in the farmhouses, twinkling here and there like tiny stars dropped down for evening visits.

"You know," he said, "it would be nice if Prince could go to one of those schools, wouldn't it? Just think. Prince Tom the Third, Companion Dog."

6

Prince won't have any trouble in Obedience School," Nathan said happily.

In the black and white station wagon, Tom and Nathan and Prince were on their way to a school that met one evening a week about twenty miles away from Adrian.

"Prince will probably be able to pass all those silly little tests after the first night," Nathan predicted. He pictured Prince in a class of ordinary dogs. The other dogs were going to look pretty dumb beside Prince, all right. "I bet the teacher's going to be surprised when he sees what a smart dog Prince is," Nathan went on. "I bet that teacher's never had such a smart dog in his class."

Tom turned the station wagon into the driveway beside a big white house. "Here we are," he said and he looked at his watch. "We're about five minutes late. Too bad we're late, Princey. The first night of school, too."

He snapped Prince's leash on his collar and opened the door. Nathan opened the door on his side, too, but he didn't seem to be in any hurry.

"Oh, don't rush," Nathan said. "The teacher won't mind if Prince is late—not as soon as he sees what kind of a dog he is." Nathan gave Prince a final pat on the head before getting out of the car. "I just hope you won't be too bored, Princey," he said.

Inside the house was a large bare room. In the middle of the room was a man who was apparently the teacher, and in a wide circle around him were about twenty dogs, each standing beside its master. There were all kinds of dogs. There was a little gray dog whose hair fell over his eyes like a mop. There was a long, low dog with a sad face and ears that scraped the floor when he walked. There were poodles and terriers, a collie, a German shepherd, and several boxers. Nathan had never seen so many different dogs at one time. He slipped into a chair at the side of the room and watched while Tom and Prince joined the circle.

Prince had never seen so many different dogs either. He looked around the room and decided that this was one of the best places Tom had ever brought him. What fun it was going to be to go around the circle with Tom and meet every one of these dogs! Prince could hardly wait to get a better look at that floppy-haired dog that didn't seem to have any eyes.

Prince pulled on his leash, eager to get started, but Tom didn't come. This was strange because Tom knew how much Prince liked to meet other dogs. Whenever Tom took him for a walk, Tom was always very considerate and allowed him to visit with all the dogs they met. Prince pulled on his leash again, but Tom didn't pay any attention. He just stood still and looked at the man in the center of the circle.

"One of the first things in obedience," the man was saying, "is to teach your dog to show no interest in other dogs. With some training your dog will not even turn his head when another dog passes."

Prince wished that Tom would stop listening to the man and listen to him. He tugged on his leash and begged Tom in his most pleading up-and-down way to come with him. But Tom was acting very queer. He looked stern and he didn't seem to understand at all.

The man in the center of the circle had a dog too— a brown dog with a plumy tail. Now he was bringing his dog to the edge of the circle and walking around it. It was just what Prince wanted to do with Tom, but Tom didn't understand.

"When I come near you with my dog," the man said, "don't allow your dog to get up. Keep him in a seated position. If he starts to get up, say 'Sit' and push him down again. And don't confuse your dog with different words for your commands. Always use a

single word if possible, and give the same command each time."

The man and the brown dog were coming close to Prince now, and Prince jumped up to meet them. He ran to the end of his leash and talked to the brown dog. Then Tom began to act very queer indeed. He jerked Prince back on his leash and held the leash short, talking to him in the strangest way. "Sit. Sit. Sit," Tom said. He had never talked to Prince like this before. He had always talked to him in the same voice he used for everyone. He would say, "Prince, you haven't played with your fire plug for a long time, have you?" Or he would say, "Prince, do you think it's time to go for a walk?" Now he was using a funny voice. "Sit," he said. "Sit, sit." He talked as if he didn't even know Prince.

Prince turned around and there was Nathan on a chair behind him. Prince wagged his tail and started to talk to Nathan, but Nathan was acting strange too. He was frowning and whispering in a loud, hissing way. "Sit, sit," he said. "Sit"—that was all anyone seemed to say. All around the circle Prince could hear the other people talking to their dogs and they were saying the same thing. "Sit, sit."

All at once all of them changed the word they were saying. "Heel," the man in the center of the circle said and then everyone was saying "Heel." Prince and Tom were walking around in the circle but in a very stupid way. They never caught up to any other dog. Each dog walked behind another dog, and every time Prince tried to run ahead and see the dog in front of him, Tom jerked him back and said, "Heel." Tom didn't seem to be pleased with anything Prince did, and Prince wasn't pleased with Tom either.

Prince tried to think of what he could do to make everything right again. He tried sitting down and talking it over with Tom, but Tom wouldn't talk. He sounded, instead, as if he were trying to bark like a dog. "Heel, heel, heel," he barked.

On the second time around the circle Prince noticed the hurdles. Three of them were lined up at the side of the room beyond the circle. They looked as if they had been made to jump over. Suddenly Prince knew how he could make things right. With a quick, strong jerk, he pulled the leash out of Tom's hand and raced over to the hurdles. He bounded into the air, his leash streaming behind him, and jumped over the first hurdle. He bounded up again and went over the second hurdle. Then he was up and over the third hurdle. He stood still and waited for Tom to laugh and for everyone else to clap.

But nobody clapped. Instead, the man at the center of the circle walked over to Prince, picked up his leash, and led him back to Tom. "Those are the hurdles for the advanced class," he said. "He'll do all right if he gets there. *If* he ever learns to obey."

Then Tom and Prince started to walk around the circle again and Tom was barking. "Heel," he said. "Heel, heel."

Prince was glad when school was over and he was back in the car with Tom and Nathan again. It was certainly nice to hear them talk in the old, familiar way.

"You didn't do so well, did you, Prince?" Tom said.

Prince wagged his tail and licked Tom's face. He rolled over on the front seat between Tom and Nathan. He sat up on his hind legs and he talked in his throat. "This is more like it," he seemed to say as Nathan hugged him. "You've always liked my ideas before. I wonder why you didn't in there."

"You know what the trouble is," Nathan said to Tom. "Prince has always had such good ideas, but in Obedience School he isn't supposed to have ideas. He's just supposed to obey."

"Maybe he isn't the kind of dog that will ever do well in obedience work," Tom said.

Nathan stuck his chin out stubbornly. "Yes, he will too," he said. "Once he catches on. Won't you, Princey?"

Prince barked twice. It sounded to Nathan as if the barks were a promise. "Yes, sir," Nathan said. "Once you catch on, you'll be the best dog there." He ruffled up the fur on top of Prince's head. "Silly old dog," he added.

7

OBEDIENCE SCHOOL was to last for twelve weeks and end with a final examination. The teacher explained that in order to pass the examination each dog would need a great deal of practice and drill between classes. Tom had planned to practice with Prince every day, but his work kept him unusually busy. He didn't have much time for practice and he even had to skip several classes.

If it hadn't been for this, Prince might have caught on sooner to what school was about. As it was, Prince didn't do very well. As soon as he came into the room each week, he realized that this was the place where everyone acted queer. The men spent all the time barking and each dog was supposed to pretend he was the only dog in the room. When there were nineteen other interesting dogs within sniffing distance, Prince had to walk around and around in a circle beside the man he saw every day of his life. Still, Prince loved

Tom very much and was willing to humor him. Prince let Tom jerk him around but tried not to listen to him bark. Instead, Prince let his mind run ahead and romp with the other dogs.

"If you'd only pay attention," Tom sighed one evening after class. "I don't see how you're going to graduate at this rate."

It wasn't that Prince did anything very wrong. He didn't break away again or go over the hurdles, but he just didn't listen. Tom had to say "Heel" several times before Prince seemed to hear. When Tom said "Stay" and walked away from Prince, Prince would stay—unless he happened to forget.

The night of the final class the teacher spoke to Tom. "You can bring your dog to the examination and graduation next week if you want to," he said. "I'm afraid he won't pass."

"Well, we'll try it," Tom decided, but on graduation night he was rather relieved that Nathan wasn't able to go along. If Prince were the only dog that didn't graduate, Nathan would feel dreadful.

At graduation Tom knew that each owner or trainer was given a number to wear on his sleeve and when his number was called, he would take his dog onto the floor and give him various commands. A dog would be judged and given points for his ability to carry out these commands quickly and well.

The long, low dog with the sad face was the first

one called for his test, and he did everything well. He sat when he was supposed to sit, he heeled the first time he was told to heel, and he stayed until he was allowed to get up.

"Watch the way the other dogs do it," Tom whispered to Prince as they sat on the side lines waiting their turn.

Prince didn't watch the dogs on the floor; he was much too interested in the dogs sitting beside him. On one side was the gray-haired dog whose hair fell into his eyes, and on the other side was a brown boxer. Prince was delighted. At last he was going to have a chance to visit. The brown boxer went away once but he came back. The floppy-haired dog went away, too, but he came back. Then, just as Prince had decided that school might turn out to be a nice place, after all, Tom called him, took him onto the floor, and began barking.

"Heel," Tom said.

Prince looked back at the gray dog and the boxer.

"Heel," Tom repeated.

Prince heard Tom this time and he moved rather lazily to the position Tom seemed to want him to take. He had to heel on the leash and heel off the leash. He had to stand and stay, to come when he was called, to sit for one minute, and to lie down for three minutes. He did everything he was supposed to, but never the first time he was told, and when he did do it, he was

slow and rather sloppy about it.

"Well, I'm certainly glad Nathan wasn't here to see that performance," Tom growled as he and Prince went back to the side lines.

As soon as every dog had had a turn on the floor, the teacher stood up in the center of the room.

"I shall read the names of the dogs and their owners in the order in which they graduate," the teacher said. "I shall begin with the dog who scored the highest on the tests and go on down the line."

The brown boxer and his owner went up first and the owner received a white diploma. A German shepherd went next. One by one all the dogs went up until at last only Prince and Tom were left.

The teacher hesitated. He picked up the diploma and held it uncertainly for a moment. Then he called Prince Tom's name.

"He scored the lowest possible number of points," the teacher told Tom privately, handing out the diploma. "Your dog's at the bottom of the class, and I'd advise you to give up the idea of trying to train him further in obedience. He's just not the type."

Tom took the diploma and walked back to his seat on the side lines. "He's not the type," he repeated to himself. "Not the type!" He remembered how Nathan had stuck out his chin when Tom had suggested that perhaps Prince would never do well in obedience work. Tom could feel his own chin sticking out now in the same way.

"Not the type!" Tom said again when he and Prince were in the station wagon on the way home. "We'll see about that. At least we'll give you a fair chance, Prince. This time it was mostly my fault."

The next day Tom bought a book about how to train dogs in obedience. He arranged his work so that every day he could take Prince to Dr. Thompson's for an hour or two of practice. At first, all Prince wanted to do was wheel Karen's doll carriage or jump over the rose bush. He couldn't understand why Tom was beginning that barking business here where they had always had so much fun. But Tom was patient. "Heel," he would say. "Heel, heel. Stay. Sit. Lie down." And he always used that sharp, loud voice that everyone used at school.

Then one day, quite by accident, when Tom started to drill Prince, he forgot about using single words and barking his commands. He began to talk softly in regular sentences, the way he always had when he told Prince to roll the barrel or put out a match or jump up into a chair.

"I want you to heel, Prince," he said. "Quickly now. Let's get a little closer. That's it, boy. That's the way."

Prince cocked his head at Tom, walked right over, and did just what he was supposed to do. When he had finished each exercise, he sat down and looked at Tom, waiting for something else to do.

"Let's try lying down," Tom said. "Don't move until I call you."

Prince flopped quickly to the ground and lay still as stone while Tom timed one minute, two minutes, then three minutes.

"All right, Prince, you can come now," Tom grinned.

Prince ran over to Tom, wagging his tail and talking in his throat. "This is fun now that you've stopped barking," he seemed to say. "It's like doing tricks, only doing them together. How come I didn't know this before?"

Nathan had been sitting on the grass, watching the practice. He jumped up and ran over to Prince and hugged him. "He's caught on," he said to Tom. "I told you he would. He's really caught on."

It was true. Prince seemed to have discovered all at once that it was fun to see how well and how quickly he could obey Tom. Before long, all Tom needed to say was, "Let's heel," very softly and Prince would jump up into the air and spin around, landing at exactly the right spot on the left side of Tom.

"I bet he could go into the Novice Obedience Trials right now and win his Companion Dog title," Nathan said. "But just for fun, why don't you try some of the more advanced exercises?"

Nathan spoke so casually, no one would have guessed all the secret ideas behind his suggestion. By this time, though, Nathan had read Tom's book on training dogs and he had discovered that Companion Dog wasn't the only title a dog could win at obedience trials. After he had won his Companion Dog title in the Novice Class, he could enter the Open Class and by winning 170 or more points three times in more difficult tests, he could win the title of Companion Dog Excellent. And that wasn't all. Once he had that title, he could go into the Utility Class and win still another title—Utility Dog. In other words, a superior dog could have three titles strung grandly out at the end of his name. Prince Tom, for instance, could become Prince Tom III, Companion Dog, Companion Dog Excellent, Utility Dog, or to use the common abbreviations, he would be Prince Tom III, C.D., C.D.X., U.D.

This was too much to hope for. Nathan didn't even mention it. He just kept his ideas in the same secret place in his mind that he kept his daydreams. But every once in a while, remembering some of the advanced exercises listed in the book, he would say, "Let's try Prince out on the broad jump." Or, "Let's try Princey out on retrieving the dumbbell."

The harder the exercises became, the more fun they were for Prince. When Tom told Prince to jump or to retrieve, it was just like going back to the tricks and the games they used to play before obedience training began. Prince not only learned quickly, he could hardly wait for his practice session to begin every day, and when it was over he begged for more.

At last Tom decided it was time to enter Prince in an advanced obedience class so that he could get used to obeying orders when there were other dogs around.

"It starts tonight," Tom told Nathan. "Prince and I will pick you up in the station wagon."

On the way over for Nathan that evening, Tom scratched Prince. "Not the type, huh?" he said. "Just not the type!"

8

When Tom and Prince walked into the obedience class, the teacher shook his head. "Haven't you got anything better to do, Mr. Clute?" he asked. "It's just a waste of time to bring that dog here."

Tom grinned at Nathan. "I have plenty of time to waste," Tom told the teacher. "So has Prince Tom. We might as well waste it here."

Tom and Prince took their place in the circle and Nathan found a chair against the wall. "Don't pay any attention to the other dogs," Tom whispered to Prince. "We're going to do our exercises, only we're going to do them better than we've ever done them before."

Prince flashed his little stump of a tail back and forth, and from where Nathan was sitting, it almost looked as if Prince winked at Tom.

"We'll start with some simple review work tonight," the teacher announced. "Heel your dog and we'll walk around the circle twice."

As soon as Tom told Prince what he wanted, Prince spun around smartly and took his position exactly where he was supposed to. He held his head high and walked proudly at just the right pace beside Tom. He halted immediately when he was told to halt. When the order was for a turn, he made his turn sharply, and when the teacher called for a Figure 8, he produced a neat and beautiful Figure 8.

The teacher walked slowly past Prince with his own brown dog with the plumy tail, but Prince paid no attention. He looked neither to the right nor to the left; he was listening too hard for Tom's next order.

Nathan wriggled in his chair, trying his best not to grin too foolishly. Prince had never done so well, he thought. He acted as if it was even more fun to do his exercises when there were other dogs around. It almost seemed as if he were trying not only to do well but to do better than any dog there. Nathan couldn't help letting his grin spread wider and wider across his face —especially as he watched the teacher.

The teacher couldn't take his eyes off Prince. He followed him around the circle. The teacher made his orders harder and harder. Finally he stopped the class and walked over to Tom.

"That isn't the same dog you had here before, is it, Clute?" he asked.

Tom grinned. "Yes, sir," he said. "It certainly is."

The teacher scratched his head. "I just don't see

how it could be," he said. "I never saw such a change." He started to walk away and then he came back. He stuck his neck out and looked hard at Tom. "Are you *sure* it's the same dog?"

"Positive," Tom answered with a chuckle, and in his chair against the wall Nathan laughed out loud.

The teacher invited Tom and Prince to the middle of the room to demonstrate some advanced work. At the end of the evening the teacher called Tom aside.

"I don't know how it happened," he said, "but your dog will be ready for trials very soon. If I were you, though, I'd give him all the advanced practice I could in school first."

"That sounds like good advice," Tom said, still smiling at the puzzled way the teacher looked at Prince.

Tom brought Prince to class faithfully every week and in order to give him still more practice in working where there were other dogs and other distractions, he also entered him in an advanced obedience class in Jackson. So Tom and Prince were going to school two evenings a week now and Prince loved it. He learned to go over a high jump and retrieve. He learned to lie down and stay for five minutes while Tom went all the way off the floor. After every new exercise, Prince cocked his head and wagged his tail vigorously back and forth. Sometimes his tail went so fast, it looked as if it were the windup part of a mechanical toy. "Try me on some more," his tail seemed to say. "I can do more. Try me. Try me."

When graduation night came, Prince Tom's name was called off first in both obedience schools. His score at one school was 195 out of a possible 200; his score at the other school was 198.

"I'd start entering him now in as many obedience trials as you can," the teacher told Tom and Nathan before they left on graduation night. "It often takes a dog a year to get enough points at three trials to win his Companion Dog title, but the more trials he enters, the more experience he gets."

That night, when Tom and Nathan got home, they looked in the American Kennel Club magazine for dates and places where obedience trials were to be held. They sent in Prince Tom's application for all the obedience trials that would take place within driving distance of Adrian. It happened that there were three trials coming up three days in a row—one in Grand Rapids on September 1, one in Lansing on September 2, and one in Kalamazoo on September 3.

"We might as well enter him in all three," Tom said to Nathan, "even if they are close together. It will at least give him experience." Tom turned to Prince. "Is that all right with you, Princey?"

Prince cocked his head and wagged his tail in his most eager try-me way.

"A trial isn't the same as school, you know," Tom

warned Prince as they practiced in Dr. Thompson's back yard.

"A trial isn't the same," Tom said again on the afternoon that he and Prince were driving to their first trial in Grand Rapids.

No, it wasn't the same. Prince could see that right away when he walked into the enormous room in Grand Rapids where the trial was to be held. Everything was bigger and better. There were more dogs and there were more people. The people sat on row after row of benches along all four sides of the room, and whenever a dog finished his exercises, the people clapped. It was like the TV show in Toledo. There was the same kind of crackling excitement in the air, too. Prince's eyes sparkled and the back half of him wig-wagged back and forth as he waited for his turn and his chance to make the people clap.

Usually the audience didn't clap until a dog had completed his tests, but it was different with Prince Tom. When his turn came, he walked out onto the floor and when Tom said "Heel," very softly, Prince did what he always did. He jumped as if a firecracker had gone off under him, whirled around in the air, and came down at precisely the correct heeling position. The audience burst out clapping. It was wonderful. Prince hadn't had so much fun since the television show. When he walked off the floor that evening, he had won third place and a score of 194½ points. The people on the benches clapped and nudged each other. "That little blond cocker!" they laughed. "What a dog!"

Tom went to the telephone and called up Nathan in Adrian. "All he needs are two more trials like tonight," he said, "and Prince will have earned his Companion Dog title."

Nathan's voice came over the wire squeaky with excitement. "Maybe he can do it tomorrow and the next day," he said. "Maybe when you come home from Kalamazoo day after tomorrow, he'll be a Companion

Dog. Maybe he'll get it in just three days. Maybe—"

Tom laughed. "Hold on, there," he interrupted. "Take it easy. Maybe he won't, too. I never heard of it happening that fast. Maybe it was just luck this time."

Tom looked down at Prince, who was sitting at his feet while he telephoned. "Maybe it wasn't luck either," Tom thought. "Maybe he really could do it. The little rascal."

The next night at Lansing there were even more people and they clapped even harder. And Prince Tom liked it even better. He took first place that night and when he went off the floor, he had a blue ribbon and a gold cup.

"See!" Nathan crowed when Tom called him up after the trial. "I told you. It wasn't luck at all. He'll do it again tomorrow. You'll see."

Tom grinned. "Maybe," he admitted. All that night and the next day until time for the trial at Kalamazoo, Tom teeter-tottered back and forth on the word "maybe." One minute he would think, maybe he won't do it. Maybe it was just luck. Then he would look at Prince and he would think, maybe he will, too. Maybe.

Back in Adrian, Nathan wasn't doing any teeter-tottering. He was sure. All day as he went about the house and the yard, he kept telling himself that Prince could do it again. He made up a little song about it that he sang privately first to his pet turtle, Jonner

Poky Thompson, and then to his pet parakeet, Winky Roy Thompson.

"Prince can do it; he can too.
He can do it at Kalamazoo."

Every once in a while Nathan would look at the clock. "Prince and Tom must be getting ready to go to the trial now," he thought, and he hummed his little tune. He looked at the clock again. "They must be at the trial." Nathan crossed his fingers and whispered to himself. "You can do it, Princey. You can do it." Nathan watched the clock until he knew the trial must be over. Then he sat very still on a white kitchen chair and waited for the telephone to ring. The clock ticked louder and louder until Nathan didn't see how he could even hear the telephone if it did ring.

But he did hear it. When it finally rang, the sound clanged through the kitchen like the bell on a fire engine. Nathan jumped to answer it and when he picked up the receiver, his fingers were still crossed. He didn't say "hello" into the phone. He didn't say "This is Dr. Thompson's residence," as he sometimes did. He just said in a very small voice that he didn't recognize as his own, "Did he do it?"

Then he smiled and uncrossed his fingers. Tom's voice boomed through the kitchen, and Nathan knew before he heard the exact words that the news was good.

"First place again," Tom said. "He's earned that title."

"I told you," Nathan said happily.

When Nathan hung up the phone, he was still smiling.

> "He did do it; he did, too.
> He did do it at Kalamazoo."

He sang it three times and then he went to the barn, where his father and Peter were.

"How does it sound?" he said. "Prince Tom the Third, Companion Dog!"

9

A DOG can't compete in the Open Class trials until he has officially received his Companion Dog title from the American Kennel Club. It was almost two months before Prince received his title. In the meantime, Tom and Prince competed in three more novice trials just for the fun of it. In all three, Prince's score never fell below 193.

"The Open Class trials for the title of Companion Dog Excellent will be harder," Tom warned Nathan. "They're judged more strictly and more experienced dogs compete."

"Pooh!" Nathan scoffed. "I'm not worried. Princey's never had a score under 190 and he won't begin now."

But not even Nathan dreamed that Prince would win the honors he did. In three shows in a row he won first place with high scores. All over America people who were interested in dogs were saying, "I hear there's a little cocker spaniel out in Michigan who's setting all kinds of records in obedience trials."

Prince Tom had a long shelf full of gold and silver cups now. One day just before Easter, 1952, after he had scored these three spectacular victories, he received something in the mail that Tom and Nathan thought was even more exciting than a gold cup. It was almost more exciting than the title of Companion Dog Excellent which, of course, Prince had won now, although Tom and Nathan were again waiting for official notification to arrive.

Nathan was in the kitchen coloring Easter eggs with Peter and Karen and Joey and Ruth when suddenly Tom and Prince burst through the back door. Prince was holding a big brown envelope in his mouth.

"Give it to Nathan, Prince," Tom said. "Go ahead. Show it to Nathan."

Nathan quickly rinsed the purple dye off his hands while Prince ran up to him, his tail switching back and forth in a half circle almost as wide as the smile on Tom's face.

As the children crowded around, Nathan looked at the outside of the envelope.

"Open it," Karen cried. Karen was the kind of person who tore the wrapping paper and broke the strings when she opened her Christmas presents. Nathan was the kind who shook the package first, felt it carefully, and then untied the bow.

"The envelope says it's from a magazine called

Dog's World," Nathan said. "Maybe Prince's picture is in the magazine!"

He opened the envelope but there was no magazine inside. Instead, there was a heavy piece of white paper with official-looking lettering. This is what it said.

AWARD OF CANINE DISTINCTION

For acquiring in competition in Open A Obedience Classes at three successive shows these high scores.

Cleveland 199, Detroit 198½, first in class; Flint 196, first in class. Tied for highest score at Cleveland. Indeed a record which deserves recognition in the annals of obedience trials.

In public recognition of this worthy record, the Committee has enrolled the award as a permanent record in its Album of Great Dogs of the Past and Present, 31st of March, 1952.

"Award of Canine Distinction. Great Dogs of the Past and Present," Nathan repeated in awe. It sounded grand and historic. It was like having someone in the family elected President. Nathan imagined all the great dogs of the past—the St. Bernards who had rescued people in the Alps, the sled dogs who had pulled their loads through arctic blizzards, the famous Seeing-eye Dogs, the great hunting dogs, and then he looked at Princey, sitting on the kitchen floor, his little stump tail swishing merrily from side to side.

"Oh, Princey," he said, "how can I love you so?"

Perhaps that wasn't the way to talk to a Great Dog of the Present, formally known as Prince Tom III, Companion Dog, Companion Dog Excellent, but Nathan's heart was too full to say anything else.

The next day was Easter, and Tom and Prince were going to Dayton to compete in another open trial. On the way they stopped at Dr. Thompson's to say good-by and found everyone out in the back yard hunting Easter eggs.

"Look at my eggs!" Ruth cried. "I found three!" She showed Tom a blue egg, a yellow egg, and a purple egg nesting in her little basket.

"I have five," Nathan called from behind the rose bush.

Prince bounced from one child to another, as busy as the Easter bunny himself. It was a beautiful day. The sky was the color of the blue egg in Ruth's basket and there were soft clouds floating here and there like puffs of apple blossom. It was the kind of day when, if you stood quite still, you knew how a tree felt with the sap rising in it. The trouble was that on a day like this you couldn't stand still—not for long.

Certainly Prince couldn't. He nosed among the flower beds, leaped over the rose bush, and galloped around the barn while the children finished their hunt and brought their baskets to the porch steps, where Tom was sitting.

"Why don't you and Prince stay here with us today?" Nathan asked Tom. "It's such a nice day. Besides, it's just another open trial you're going to. What else can Prince do in an open trial that he hasn't done already?"

Tom shrugged his shoulders. "Nothing, I guess," he said. "But until he can enter the Utility Class, we might as well keep in practice."

"I bet Princey would rather stay here." Nathan turned to ask Prince if this wasn't true, but Prince wasn't in sight. "Where did he go?" Nathan asked.

"The other side of the barn, I think," Tom said and he whistled.

Usually Prince couldn't run fast enough to answer Tom's whistle, but this time he came slowly around the side of the barn. He seemed to walk carefully, holding his head high as if he were carrying something in his mouth. He came straight to Tom, lowered his head, and laid at Tom's feet a bright red Easter egg.

"Oh, look!" Karen cried. "He found one we missed!"

"I bet he thinks he found a new kind of ball," Peter said. While everyone laughed and exclaimed, Prince sat in front of Tom, cocked his head from side to side and talked in his throat—long paragraphs of up-and-down talk.

"What's he saying?" Joey asked.

Tom scratched his head. "You know," he said, "he's been talking a lot lately. And he's been bringing me things like this. He's always nosing around the house and bringing me something."

"I know what he's saying," Nathan said. "He's showing you he knows all about retrieving and he doesn't need to go today."

"He's saying he wants to stay here," Karen said, "and hunt eggs. We can hide them all over again."

Nathan grinned. "There isn't one thing you can do at that trial that you haven't already done. Is there, Princey?"

Prince didn't seem to agree. He was wagging his tail and bouncing up and down, which usually meant, "Come on. Try me. Try me."

Nathan looked surprised. "You don't really want to go, do you, Prince?"

In answer, Prince turned and ran to the black and white station wagon.

10

Nathan was wrong. There was something Prince could do that he had never done before, and he did it that afternoon. He made a perfect score of 200. "The almost impossible perfect score," the newspaper reported the next day, ". . . as rare as a no-hitter in a baseball game. . . . The first perfect score of the year."

Prince went on distinguishing himself in Open Trials all spring. Tom took him to Canada, where he competed in three shows, scoring a perfect 200 again in Ontario. "Prince Tom is the only dog to register perfect scores in both United States and Canada," the paper said that time. "The exceptional showing earned him the title of 'International Dog Champion.'"

After the Canadian trip, Tom and Prince concentrated more and more on practice for the utility trials. In utility work, commands are not spoken. Hand signals are used instead. Prince enjoyed the practice—especially when it had anything to do with retrieving. Even when practice was over for the day, Prince didn't want to stop retrieving. He would look around the house for something to bring Tom and then he would beg Tom to hide it. Tom had to keep all the closet doors shut tightly. Otherwise Prince would nose them open and bring out anything he could find on the closet floor.

"I believe that dog would rather retrieve than eat," Tom laughed one day. "In fact, I wouldn't be surprised if sometime, instead of eating his food, he brought me his dish and asked me to hide it."

Prince started his utility trials in the winter. Tom and Nathan were both sure he would do well. Still, Tom shook his head as he spoke to Nathan while they were waiting their turn at the first trial.

"I don't know what's got into that dog," Tom said. "He'll do all right if he doesn't take it into his head to retrieve everything on the floor."

Nathan nodded. It was true that Prince was wonderful at retrieving. The judges at all the open trials had been amazed when Tom would throw a dumbbell sixty or seventy feet instead of the required forty or fifty and still Prince would have no trouble finding it and returning it.

"But that's not what we're doing now, Princey," Nathan explained, taking Prince's head between his hands. "Now you're in the Utility Class, not the Open Class. There won't be any dumbbell throwing. There'll be retrieving of course, but you'll have to be very careful about it. You mustn't pick up everything. Five metal objects, five wooden objects, five leather objects will be placed on the floor. Your job will be to pick out the last one handled by Tom."

Prince blinked his eyes politely as much as to say, "Thank you very much but I knew that all the time."

And he did know it. At every utility trial in which he competed, he brought home a new gold cup or silver cup or blue ribbon. By the following spring he was officially a Utility Dog.

The wall in Nathan's room was covered with pictures of Prince and newspaper clippings, and above the pictures and clippings was a long strip of cardboard with Nathan's printing on it. Nathan had put up the strip of cardboard when Prince entered his novice trials and he had made the strip long on purpose, even though at first there wasn't much printing on it. The printing was on the left side with a long blank space after it.

When he first put it up, it looked like this.

PRINCE TOM III

Then it looked like this.

PRINCE TOM III, C.D.

Later it looked like this.

```
PRINCE TOM III, C.D., C.D.X.
```

Now it looked like this.

```
PRINCE TOM III, C.D., C.D.X., U.D.
```

Every morning when Nathan woke up, he looked first at Princey's pictures and the long strip of cardboard with the letters all the way across. "Princey did it," he would think. "He did it all. Everything he could." And Nathan would feel warm and happy and proud. Sometimes he would lie in bed and whisper Princey's full name to himself, just to hear the glorious sound of it all. "Prince Tom the Third, Companion Dog, Companion Dog Excellent, Utility Dog." Sometimes he would pretend he was introducing Prince to an important official—a foreign nobleman or a visiting king, perhaps—when it would be improper not to use Prince's complete, official name with all the titles. Then after Nathan had finished with the full name, he would often add in a casual, explaining way, "Oh yes, he is also International Dog Champion, and his name appears in the *Album of Great Dogs of the Past and Present*."

Now that Prince had won all his titles, Tom planned

to relax. The trials had been fun, but it would be fun, too, to take it easy with Prince—no more practice sessions, no more long drives to Akron and Dayton and Kalamazoo and Canada, although he and Prince might still enter a trial once in a while if it was nearby.

"You've got enough cups now," Tom said to Prince one evening. "We'll just live like ordinary people again —eh, Princey?" Tom stretched out his legs, leaned back in the armchair, and closed his eyes. He reached his hand down lazily to scratch Prince, but Prince wasn't there.

Prince didn't like the lazy sound of Tom's voice. He wasn't sure what Tom had said, but he didn't think he agreed with it. His ideas at the moment were much more active; he was looking for a crack. From closet to closet all over the house he ran, and at last he found the door of Tom's bedroom closet open a crack and he went to work. He opened the closet door and, one by one, he brought downstairs and laid at Tom's feet two pairs of shoes, a pair of sneakers, a pair of bedroom slippers, and a pair of fishing boots. When he had finished, he sat down and barked for Tom to wake up. He wagged his tail furiously from side to side, the way he always did when he had an idea. "I can do more," he seemed to say. "Don't get lazy. Try me. Try me."

Tom laughed. "You don't like the idea of taking it easy, do you, Princey?"

Prince sat up straight and speeded up his tail.

"What more do you think you can do?" Tom asked. "Do you want to open up a shoe store?" Tom pulled himself heavily out of the armchair. "O.K., O.K. Bury your head and I'll hide the shoes for you to retrieve. Just once."

Prince put his front paws up on the chair and put his head down between them. He wondered if Tom really had understood. Because if Tom didn't think of any new retrieving ideas, Prince would have to.

All summer long Prince thought up new ideas. Sometimes they were good ideas and sometimes they weren't. Once when Tom was reading the evening paper on the porch and Prince was supposed to be taking a nap at his feet, he had a wonderful idea. Tom didn't notice him quietly coming and going, coming and going, but ten minutes later Tom looked up and saw Prince trotting up the walk with a rolled-up newspaper in his mouth. He had been to six houses on Dennis Street and he had retrieved six papers. They lay in a neat row on Tom's porch.

Another time Tom and Prince and all the Thompsons were having a picnic beside the little pond at the end of the pasture. After the picnic, Nathan picked up his softball and bat, and everyone spread out over the field for a game—everyone but Prince. No one had thought of giving Prince a part in the game, so he sat on the side lines and cocked his head this way and that. He watched the ball fly back and forth from one person to another. Then he noticed that sometimes the ball flew way out where there was no one to get it. That gave Prince his idea. He ran out across the field beyond everyone else and whenever a ball came his way, Prince would go after it. No matter how far it went nor how high the grass was where it fell, Prince would find it and bring it back. After that, Prince was permanent outfielder for every ball game at the Thompsons'.

Prince wasn't the only one to get ideas. At one of these ball games the first beginning of an idea came to Dr. Thompson. It was just a little seed of an idea, not big enough even to mention out loud. Prince had just chased a home-run ball that Tom had hit into the cornfield. Dr. Thompson watched Prince bring the ball back. He leaped through the tall grasses—his ears streaming behind him, his head high—and when Peter, who was pitcher, called him, Prince laid the ball gently at his feet.

"I wonder," Dr. Thompson said softly to himself. "I wonder."

11

SOMETIMES an idea really is like a seed, growing underground where no one can see it for a long time and then one day suddenly popping into sight. Dr. Thompson's idea was like that. Whenever he saw Prince running across the field with a ball in his mouth, the doctor's idea grew a little, although not even he could really see it yet. It wasn't until the afternoon that Nathan's turtle, Jonner Poky Thompson, ran away that Dr. Thompson's idea popped into the open.

It was a crisp fall day, the kind of day that makes everyone feel able to stride across the top of the world without getting tired. Because it was this kind of day, Dr. Thompson was in the tool shed oiling his gun and thinking about hunting and the hillside below the cornfield. Maybe because it was this kind of day, Jonner Poky Thompson slipped out of the kitchen door when no one was looking and disappeared.

Nathan was the first to discover that he was missing.

Nathan looked all around the outside of the house, in the flower beds, under the rose bush. "He's so slow and poky, he can't have gone far," he thought.

"Jonner Poky Thompson," he called softly as he crawled around the back yard on his hands and knees. "Jonner Poky Thompson."

Peter and Karen and Joey and Ruth came out to help look. They got down on their hands and knees too. Dr. Thompson came out of the tool shed and he got down on his hands and knees.

When Tom and Prince drove up in the black and white station wagon, the Thompson family looked as if they were playing a game. They almost looked as if they were pretending to be dogs, although they were doing it very awkwardly. Prince bounded out of the car and ran from one to another, showing them how to manage on four legs. In a moment, however, Prince realized that no one was playing a game. Ruth was crying. Nathan's mouth was closed as tightly as a closet door without an opening crack. Everyone was looking worried and unhappy.

Dr. Thompson stood up as Tom came toward him. "Nathan's turtle has disappeared," he said. "He seems to be gone for good." He turned to Nathan. "I'm afraid we're not going to find him, Nathan. We'll get you another one."

Nathan opened his mouth just a slit. "I don't want

another one," he mumbled. "I want Jonner Poky Thompson."

Nathan was on his hands and knees again, hunting, and Prince followed. He gave Nathan's face a lick from time to time to let him know that whatever was the matter, he would like to help if only he knew what to do. But Nathan didn't tell him what to do. He put his arms around Prince once, buried his face in Prince's fur, but he didn't say anything. He just made a kind of quick sniffing noise and then went on crawling about, poking under bushes, looking into shadows.

Prince decided that the only thing he could do was to copy Nathan. He would poke under bushes too and sniff into shadows. He went over to the barn and began poking. He was doing everything just the way Nathan did, when he came upon a big pile of raked-up leaves. He sniffed into it and then he forgot all about copying Nathan. There was an interesting smell under those leaves, and as he listened, he thought he could hear the smell move.

He put his nose down to the ground and followed the smell through the crackling red and gold leaves—slowly and carefully until he found what he was hunting for. Something round and black and alive was creeping through the leaves. Prince opened his mouth, picked it up, and carried it gently to Nathan.

Nathan's mouth was still tight and closed-looking as Prince trotted up to him. It didn't change until Prince laid the black thing down. Then instead of opening his mouth just a crack, Nathan opened it all the way, as wide as he could. It was like flinging a door open suddenly.

"Jonner Poky Thompson!" he cried. "Princey found Jonner!"

As everyone rushed up to see, Nathan held his turtle and stroked his hard, black back. "He's not hurt one bit. He's just fine."

Dr. Thompson grinned and looked at Prince. And then, at just that moment, the idea that had been growing deep in his mind without his knowing it popped into the open.

"Say," he said, "I bet Prince would make a good hunting dog. He has a good nose and if he's not afraid to pick up a turtle—I'm sure he can learn to hunt." He slapped Tom enthusiastically across the shoulders. "How about it, Tom?" he said. "I've been wanting to go hunting. Let's try him out right now. Down below the cornfield."

Tom looked doubtful. "I don't know anything about hunting," he said. "I didn't know cocker spaniels were supposed to hunt. Are they?"

"Sure they are," Dr. Thompson said. "That's how they got their name. In England the little spaniel was used to hunt woodcock. So he was called a cocker. I've never seen a cocker hunt but I've heard they're good gun dogs. Let's try him. Just for an hour or so."

Prince bounced up and down in front of Tom and wagged his tail.

"I suppose that means you want to go, Princey," Tom said. "O.K. Let's try it."

Dr. Thompson turned to Nathan, who was sitting on the ground, holding his turtle on his lap. "Do you want to come along, Nathan?"

Nathan shook his head. He hadn't wanted to go to town with his mother and the other children when they had left a few minutes ago. And he didn't feel like walking around and chasing anything either. He just wanted to be quiet and play with Jonner Poky Thompson for a while. Maybe he and Jonner would go into the house and he would let Winky Roy Thompson out of his cage and the three of them would be together.

Nathan patted Prince. "Thank you, Prince. Thank you *so* much for finding Jonner. Now you go and have a good time hunting."

Nathan went into the house.

It was nice sometimes to be alone with just Winky and Jonner, Nathan thought. He let Winky out of his cage and he sat down on the living room floor to listen to the quietness. Most of the time it was fun to have people in the house and a lot of noise, but once in a while it was good to know that you could walk into

any room and say anything you wanted to and no one would disagree. It was good to know that you could do whatever you wanted and no one would tell you to do it differently. It was like being a king in a castle. And as long as Winky and Jonner were there, you didn't feel lonely.

Nathan watched Winky and Jonner. They had never played together the way they were now. It was almost as if they had made up a game. Jonner sat on the floor with his head pulled in as if he were pretending to be a rock. Then Winky swooped down onto his back. Maybe Jonner wasn't a rock at all, Nathan thought. Maybe he was a parked taxi. As soon as Winky landed on his back, Jonner poked his head out and glanced back. "Oh, I have a passenger, have I?" he seemed to say. "Where to this time?" And off he would lumber on his short, slow legs. Sometimes Winky sang to Jonner as they traveled; sometimes he repeated over and over the only word he knew—"pretty, pretty, pretty."

Nathan hoped they would keep on playing so his father and Tom and Prince could see them. He wished the three of them would come back. He wondered how Prince was liking his hunting trip. Maybe Prince would play taxi too. He would certainly be a faster taxi than Jonner.

It seemed a long time, but at last there were voices in the back yard. Nathan ran to the door.

"How did Prince do?" he called.

"He had a good time," Dr. Thompson said, "but he didn't find anything."

"Maybe there wasn't anything there to find," Nathan suggested as they all came into the kitchen.

Dr. Thompson and Tom took off their jackets and hung them on the back of a kitchen chair while Prince did what he always did when he came into the Thompson house. He started his usual tour, going from room to room to see who was home.

"Maybe Princey just isn't a bird dog," Tom said.

"Maybe not," Dr. Thompson agreed, washing his hands in the kitchen sink.

Nathan wished they would hurry. He wanted to take them into the living room to see Winky and Jonner. He wanted to take Prince too.

Prince was coming back into the kitchen now. He was holding his head high and his mouth was slightly open. He walked up to Dr. Thompson, lowered his head, and opened his mouth wide. There on the floor was Winky Roy Thompson, cheeping and fluttering his damp blue feathers.

Dr. Thompson picked up Winky quickly. While Tom and Nathan looked anxiously over his shoulder, the doctor went over Winky, feather by feather, as carefully as if he had been a patient in the hospital.

"He's not hurt at all," he said. "Only mad."

He handed Winky to Nathan. "Better put him back in his cage until he dries out."

"Oh, poor Winky!" Nathan said. "But don't be mad at Prince, Winky. He was just playing too."

As Nathan went out of the kitchen, he heard his father and Tom burst out laughing.

"Who says Prince isn't a bird dog?" Dr. Thompson said.

12

D<small>R.</small> T<small>HOMPSON</small> became more and more convinced
that Prince would make a good hunting dog if he
could have the right training. Several times Prince
found pheasants on the hillside below the cornfield,
but, of course, he didn't know that Dr. Thompson was
interested in pheasants. He didn't know that what he
was supposed to do was to find the pheasant, scare it
out of its hiding place, wait for Dr. Thompson to shoot
it and give the command to retrieve. To Prince, finding a pheasant under a brambly bush was like finding
a turtle in a pile of leaves or a parakeet in a living
room. He just went after it. When the pheasant took
to the air, Prince tried to take to the air too. He leaped
from the ground; he streaked over the fields.

"Someday that dog is going to take off and fly after
one of those birds," Dr. Thompson laughed.

Prince Tom did everything he could to catch a
pheasant, and even though he wasn't successful, even

though he soon discovered that a pheasant wasn't the same as a turtle or a parakeet—he still loved to try. He would come dashing back breathless after a chase, and his eyes would snap with excitement and his little tail would beat from side to side. "Let's try it again," he seemed to say. "Let's do it some more. Let's never give up."

"You know what I think," Nathan said one day when he was on the hillside with his father and Tom. "I think this is what Princey has been trying to tell us all along. He acts as if this is what he's always wanted to do. Almost as if he knows that in all the world this is what he's best at."

Nathan and his father and Tom watched Prince follow a trail ahead of them. He zigzagged back and forth, speeding up as the scent he was tracking became stronger and clearer. Then, as a pheasant flew up from a bush, Prince plunged headlong after it, jumping and straining and rearing into the air as the bird rose out of reach.

"Maybe you're right," Tom said thoughtfully.

"Maybe you are," Dr. Thompson agreed. "I think we should take Prince to some spaniel club around here and get some instruction or advice on how to train him for hunting before I try to shoot. We shouldn't try to teach him anything until we know the right way to do it."

The headquarters of the nearest spaniel club was a

hunting lodge out in the country. When Nathan and his father and Tom and Prince drove up to the lodge the next weekend, three men were on the porch. All three were dressed in gabardine jackets with leather on the elbows, special plastic-covered trousers, and high leather boots. Two of the men had red caps and one of them had a Tyrolean hat with special buttons and feathers stuck all over it. Each of the men had a leash, at the end of which was a large brown and white springer spaniel.

Prince looked suddenly very small as he walked up the porch steps on the end of his leash. Tom in his old khaki jacket and everyday shoes didn't look much like a hunter.

Tom stepped up to the three men and introduced himself.

"I'd like to inquire about entering my cocker in your spaniel club," he said. "I thought perhaps there would be someone here who could give me advice on training both my dog and me for hunting."

The three men looked very big standing on the porch in their heavy boots. The three springer spaniels looked tall and sure of themselves as they poked their noses at Prince and sniffed him.

"Has your dog ever hunted?" one of the men asked.

"No," Tom said, "but if there are pheasant around, he finds them. I didn't want to try to train him until I was sure I was doing it the right way."

The three men shook their heads. "He's pretty small," one of the men said.

"Even for a cocker, he's small," another agreed.

"Have there been any hunters in his background?" the third man asked. "Any other dogs in his family that have done well hunting?"

Tom shook his head. "No. He's the only dog in his family that's ever been more than a good pet."

"He's a Companion Dog," Nathan added proudly, "a Companion Dog Excellent, and a Utility Dog." Now those three men would stop looking at Prince as if he were just *any* dog, Nathan thought.

But instead of smiling and looking surprised and saying "Oh, well—if *that's* the case—" the way Nathan expected them to, the three men looked bigger and taller than ever. And they went on shaking their heads.

"Too bad," one of the men said. "Too bad you spoiled him with obedience training. Obedience dogs never make good hunters."

"That's right," another man agreed. "It's a shame he couldn't have been a *real* dog."

There was a hot, prickly feeling in the back of Nathan's neck and a hard, lumpy feeling in the bottom of his stomach. He looked at Tom, whose face was a dark red. Maybe his stomach was lumpy too, Nathan thought.

"I'm not sure what you mean by a *real* dog," Tom said. His voice sounded as if he were holding it on a tight leash. "But we'd like to join the Spaniel Club. If you have training classes, we'd like to take them. I think maybe this dog might surprise you."

The three men looked as if they had never been surprised in their lives, but they smiled pleasantly. "Sure thing," one of them said. "There's a book inside the lodge on elementary spaniel field training. I'll get it and you can take it home with you. That will give you all the instructions you'll need for the first part of his training. After that, if you want to go on with it— come back and we'll help you with more field work and water practice.

Tom took the book and the three men strode off into the fields with their three big springer spaniels. Nathan and his father, Tom and Prince climbed quietly back into the black and white station wagon.

Nathan sat in the back seat with Prince. He opened the book on spaniel field training and looked through the pages. "*Real* dog!" he muttered. "Those men don't know a real dog when they see one."

All at once Nathan stopped turning pages. "Say," he said, "did you know there are field trials for hunting dogs? Like obedience trials? There's even a national field trial to pick the champion dog of the whole country."

13

It didn't take Prince long to learn that when he went out into the field, Tom wanted him to follow a zigzag course. He would go about thirty yards to Tom's left and then cross over and go about thirty yards to Tom's right. He had been doing this, which in hunting language is called quartering, more or less on his own, but now Prince knew that when Tom blew a whistle one blast, he was supposed to change direction. If he was going to Tom's left when the whistle blew, he should turn and go to his right. When Tom blew the whistle two blasts, Prince was supposed to look back to Tom for a hand signal that would tell him what to do next. He learned that when a gun was fired, he was to sit immediately and not move until he was told to. All of this Prince learned when there happened to be no pheasants around.

Then one day Prince was following his zigzag course on the hillside below the cornfield, and there was a pheasant. Prince picked up the scent and followed it into a big brier patch. Maybe this time he could get it. He caught a glimpse of brown and gold feathers, but when he came close, the pheasant flew up in front of his nose. Prince was about to leap into the air after it as he had always done, but at that moment the gun was fired.

Prince sat down. He didn't want to, but he did. He couldn't understand why Tom wouldn't let him chase the pheasant. Then a strange thing happened. The pheasant, instead of flying out of sight, dropped suddenly to the ground. Prince looked back at Tom to see if he'd noticed it. And there was Tom signaling him to retrieve! Prince could hardly believe his luck. He took off like a thunderbolt for the place the bird had fallen. It was there, all right. Prince picked it up and carried it to Tom.

"That's the way, Princey," Tom said, taking the bird from him. "This is the way we'll do it together from now on. Do you think it's a good idea?"

Prince pumped his tail from side to side so fast that Tom had to laugh.

"O.K., O.K.," he said. "I gather you approve."

Nathan and his father, Tom and Prince went down below the cornfield every weekend. Then one weekend Dr. Thompson said he thought Prince was ready to go back to the hunting lodge.

"I hope Prince can go hunting with those three springer spaniels," Nathan said. "I bet he'd find pheasants before any of those old spaniels even got their noses to the ground."

When they reached the lodge, they found that no one was going out to the fields to hunt. Tom was told to go to the pond, where a group of men were giving their spaniels water practice. The three men they had talked to the first time were there with their spaniels.

"Hi," the man with the Tyrolean hat called in a friendly way, as though he didn't know he had made Tom and Nathan mad before. "Come on and watch how water work is done. If you think you can get your dog into the water, you can try it."

It was an unusually cold day. Even inside his warm winter jacket, Nathan shivered as he looked at the pond. A man had a boat full of birds whose wings had been clipped so they couldn't fly and he was putting the birds into the water. But the dogs wouldn't even look at them. When they were told to go in they just hung back on the shore and looked unhappy. Nathan didn't blame them. The big springer spaniel that belonged to the man with the Tyrolean hat ran up and down the bank when he was told to go in.

"This kind of weather it's hard to get a dog to go in," the man explained as he finally pushed his dog into the water.

Nathan remembered what the spaniel field training book had said. "Start your dog when the water is warm. If you have trouble, one good way is to take the dog in swimming with you. If he won't follow you into the water, carry him out so that he has to swim a short distance to the shore. It may be necessary to carry him in again before he becomes accustomed to the water."

As far as Nathan knew, Prince had never been in the water. Maybe he didn't even know how to swim. Nathan started to whisper to Tom that perhaps it would be better to wait until summer to train Prince for the water. He and Prince would go in swimming together and Prince could get used to it gradually.

Then Nathan looked at Prince. Everyone else was looking at him too.

Prince was talking in his throat in a wild, excited way. He couldn't seem to sit still. His front legs were tensed as if he were getting ready for a fast take-off.

His hind legs trembled with eagerness. And all the time he was looking at the bird floating in the water and at the unhappy spaniel paddling slowly toward it.

The man in the Tyrolean hat stared at Prince as if he couldn't believe what he saw.

"Why, I believe that little cocker *wants* to try," he said. "Let's throw the next bird out for him and see what he does."

The shivering springer brought in his bird. Then while the man in the boat got ready to throw in another, Tom leaned down and unsnapped Prince's leash. As the bird hit the water, Tom gave his order.

"Go get it, Prince," he said.

Prince leaped into the air. His eyes blazing with excitement, he stretched into a long, broad jump and landed fifteen feet out in the water. He swam right to the bird, picked it up, and swam directly back to Tom.

Prince dropped the bird in front of Tom, but before anyone realized what he was going to do, he whipped around and leaped into the water again, looking for another bird.

"Throw in another bird," the man in the Tyrolean hat called excitedly. "Throw another one in." He turned to Tom. "You never let a dog go in without bringing back something."

When Prince came out of the water with his second bird, Tom was ready for him. He snapped his leash on quickly and gave him the order to sit.

The Spaniel Club members crowded around Tom and Prince. "What a dog!" they exclaimed. "Have you ever entered him in field or water trials?"

Tom looked surprised. "Why, no," he said. "We're just learning. We came here for some help. I never thought of entering trials. Prince just seemed to like the idea of hunting, and I thought I'd go along with him for the fun of it."

The man in the Tyrolean hat grinned. "Did I say an obedience dog couldn't be made into a field dog?" He shook his head in amazement. "I never saw anything like it. He has the heart and spirit that make a great hunter." He turned to the other men. "Do you know something? That little cocker is a *real* dog."

14

THE MEN at the Spaniel Club took as much interest in Prince as if they had discovered him themselves. They insisted that Tom bring him to the lodge every weekend so that they could help with his training. Whenever Prince made an unusual retrieve, they slapped each other on the back and went home and boasted about him. "You can't fool that little cocker," they would laugh. "He's not scared of a thing."

The next fall they persuaded Tom to enter Prince in some of the field trials that were being held in the Middle West. Whenever the men from the Spaniel Club could go, they went along and watched the trials.

Nathan and Tom discovered that in a field trial two dogs hunt at the same time while judges follow, scoring them on their ability to find (or flush) a bird, to hold steady during gunfire, to retrieve on command. There are usually several problems the dogs are given to work out on land. These are called land series, and there is often a water series too. A professional gunner does the shooting, and the owner's job is to tell the dog what to do. When all the dogs have competed, the judges add up the scores and announce the winners.

Prince's Spaniel Club friends would follow along with other spectators behind the judges and wink at each other as time and again Prince surprised everyone with his performance. At the end of a trial the Spaniel Club members would go to the central hunting lodge where announcement of the winners was made. The Spaniel Club men would lean casually against the walls of the big lodge room while the judges discussed the entries and added up the scores. All the time the judges were talking, the Spaniel Club men would look knowingly at each other. "We know who the winner is," they seemed to be saying. "Why bother to add up those scores?"

Usually the Spaniel Club men were right. Prince Tom won enough field trials so that he was qualified to enter the National Trials for cocker spaniels.

"Send Prince's name in," the men urged Tom one day when they were sitting around the club after a morning of field work.

"For the National Field Trial?" Tom looked doubtful. Prince had done well in local trials, but this was different. This was *national*. It sounded very big.

"Go ahead," the men insisted. "Prince can win anything."

The National Trials were to be held in New Jersey that year. Tom had never been to New Jersey. He tried to imagine what hunting in New Jersey would be like. Somehow, even though he knew better, pictures of enormous swamps and thick undergrowth flashed through his mind.

Tom shook his head. "New Jersey is too far away," he said.

The men from the Spaniel Club exchanged secret glances. Tom was sitting in front of the fireplace, staring into the fire, so he didn't notice. The men leaned against the mantel and looked down at Tom. One of the men pointed at Prince.

"Look at that dog!" he said. Prince was sitting on a chair by the window looking outside. It was clear that Prince thought being inside the lodge was a poor idea. The little hump on his ears rose and his tail twitched as he caught a glimpse of something that might prove interesting if he were only outside to investigate.

"Look at that dog," the man repeated. "You want to be fair to Prince, don't you?"

Tom shifted uneasily in his chair. It was certainly true that Prince loved to hunt. He couldn't ride in a car without watching out the window for birds. As soon as Tom and Prince left Adrian in the black and white station wagon, Prince would start looking. Whenever he saw anything with wings, Prince would almost go through the windshield. Then he would turn around and scold Tom for not stopping. Once when they had been driving near an airport, Prince had wanted to go after a plane that was taking off.

"That is one thing you can't manage," Tom had laughed. But Prince had wagged his tail. "I could try," he seemed to say. "I could always try."

Maybe he would like to try for the National Championship, too, Tom thought. But then again, he didn't know. It might be just as silly to take Prince to New Jersey as it would be to send him after a plane.

"An American cocker has never won the National Field Trial," Tom reminded the Spaniel Club men. "The winners have always been English-born spaniels specially bred for hunting. Their fathers and mothers and grandfathers and grandmothers were all well-known hunting dogs. Look at Prince. No one in his family has ever hunted."

The men smiled.

"Besides," Tom went on, "the people who compete in the national trials *know* so much. They hire special men just to take care of their dogs and train them. They have kennels full of expensive dogs. They're *professionals*."

The men nodded. This was true, they agreed, but they didn't look convinced. Instead, they looked as if they were laughing at some private joke of their own.

One of the men put his hands in his pockets and looked at the ceiling. "It seems to me that I remember," he said slowly, "we were told once that this little cocker might surprise us."

"It seems to me," another man grinned, "it's our turn now to say the same thing. That little cocker of yours, Tom, might even surprise *you*."

"You ought to give him a chance," a third man added. "It would only be fair to give him a chance."

Tom stood up and walked over to Prince. He put his hand on Prince's back and felt the quivers of excitement run up and down as something moved in a bush outside.

"Well," Tom said, "we'll think about it."

Tom thought about it all that day. He talked it over with his mother. He even dreamed about it that night. Only in his dream he wasn't in New Jersey. He and Prince were in Africa and Prince was chasing a lion. Tom tossed back and forth on his bed. "No, Prince, no," he moaned in his sleep. "Come back, come back."

But Prince didn't come back. The three Spaniel Club men, wearing enormous pith helmets and wide seven-league boots, stepped into his dream. "Oh, let him go," they said. "Let him have his chance. It would only be fair."

"Give him his chance. It would only be fair." The words were repeated over and over in Tom's dream like a broken record.

They were repeated the next day too, but then Tom was wide awake. Everyone he asked for an opinion

about entering Prince in the National Field Trial said the same thing. "Give him a chance."

Later that day Tom drove out to ask Nathan and Dr. Thompson what they thought. He found them painting the barn.

Nathan was on the ground, painting the lower part, and his father was on a ladder, painting the upper part. Nathan dipped his brush in the can. The paint was just the right color of red, he thought. It wasn't a bright, exciting red that would make a cow nervous. It was a deep, comfortable red—the color the earth sometimes is when you dig down and turn it over. Nathan brushed the paint on in long, even strokes from side to side.

Tom walked over to the foot of the ladder to talk to Dr. Thompson. "What do you think?" he asked. "Do you think I should do it? Do you really think I should enter Prince in the Nationals?"

Nathan's brush forgot about the long, even strokes. It went back and forth unsteadily in short, interrupted jerks. "The National Field Trial Championship," Nathan said to himself. It was just what he had wanted for Prince. He held his breath, hoping that everyone would say exactly the right thing.

"I think it's a good idea," Dr. Thompson said from the top of the ladder. "I think you ought to give Prince the chance anyway. Seems kind of unfair not to give him the chance."

Nathan dipped his brush into the paint can. He slapped a great brushful of beautiful, dripping red paint against the side of the barn. He would have to find a longer piece of cardboard for his bedroom, he thought happily. A piece long enough to add Prince's new title when he became National Field Trial Champion. Nathan pictured the cardboard with the letters all filled in.

```
PRINCE TOM III, C.D., C.D.X., U.D., N.F.T.C.
```

If he won, Nathan corrected himself.

"What do you think about it, Nathan?" Tom asked.

Nathan tried to spread the dripping trickles of the paint he had slapped on into an even stroke.

"I think you have to be fair," he said. "You have to give Princey a chance."

15

Tom sent in Prince's application for the National Field Trial Championship. After he had done it, he still wondered and worried. Even the morning he and Prince were to start out in the station wagon for New Jersey, Tom was wondering if he and Princey were going to look silly beside all those English spaniels and all those professional dog handlers.

Nathan and Dr. Thompson came to Dennis Street to see Tom and Prince off. They stood on the sidewalk and watched Tom carry his suitcase out to the car. Prince was already in the front seat, two paws on the dashboard, his tail wagging hurry-up signals.

Suddenly Nathan, too, felt afraid. Suppose everyone in New Jersey made fun of Princey. Suppose the other dogs were really much, much better. Nathan dug his hands deep into his pockets and tried not to think about it. His fingers closed around the little lucky silver horseshoe that always lay at the bottom of one of his pockets. He had found it lying on the curb one day on his way to school, and on that very day his mark in a spelling test was one hundred. All at once Nathan had an idea. He took the horseshoe out of his pocket, leaned into the front seat, and snapped it onto Prince's collar.

"That's for you, Princey," he whispered. "Good luck."

Nathan didn't tell anyone what he was doing because it might spoil the luck, but right away he felt better.

"Everything's going to be all right," he said to Tom. "You wait and see."

Then he and his father waved good-by and the black and white station wagon drove off along Dennis Street.

Prince took his usual position beside the window so he could watch for birds and birdy-looking places. Every time he saw a likely place, he bounced up and down and begged Tom to stop for a hunt. But Tom didn't stop. He didn't even slow down. Not in Michigan. Not in Ohio. Not in Pennsylvania. Even when a wild goose flew over the car and Prince *ordered* Tom to stop, Tom didn't do a thing about it.

"Wait until you get to New Jersey," Tom said. "You'll get your share of hunting."

They reached New Jersey the next day, after spending the night at a motel in Pennsylvania. Tom looked out the window at the rolling brown countryside. New

Jersey didn't look much different from Michigan or Ohio, he thought. Maybe everything would be all right, after all.

But that night Tom was sure nothing would be right. He and Prince were staying in a motel near the place where the trials were to start the next morning. Prince was asleep on the foot of Tom's bed, but Tom wasn't asleep. He was thinking of all the things that could go wrong in a trial. And then something happened which he had never even thought to worry about.

It started to rain. The rain came down all at once, as if it had been holding back for months and couldn't wait any longer. It hammered on the roof of the motel, slapped against the windows, beat on the door. Tom cringed, as if he himself had been hit. Rain was the one thing he hadn't prepared for. He and Prince had never tried to hunt in the rain. The trials they had entered had always happened to be run in good weather.

Tom got up and looked out the window. In the red glow from the neon motel sign, he could see the ground already churned into mud. He remembered a sentence he had once read in a book. He didn't know the name of the book, but he could see the words printed on the left-hand page as clearly as if he had just put the book down. "Some dogs," the book said, "lose their sense of smell in the rain."

Tom looked at Prince, sleeping peacefully through the storm, his ears drooping over his face as carelessly as if tomorrow were just *any* day. Tom felt like waking Prince up. He felt like shouting the question that was going over and over in his mind. "How is your sense of smell?" he wanted to ask Prince. "Wake up and tell me. How is it?"

Next morning the rain was still coming down when Tom and Prince arrived at the hunting lodge for the trials. The lodge looked very much like other hunting lodges. A row of freshly killed pheasants hung by their feet across the front of the porch. A large deer's head was nailed on the wall. Still, Tom was too concerned about the rain to notice anything. He hardly looked at the judges and the group of men and dogs gathered, ready to start the land series.

But as Tom approached, the men looked at him. Then they looked at Prince.

"You entering that little dog?" one of the men said to Tom. A quirk of a smile twitched at the corner of the man's mouth.

"Well, here it comes," Tom thought. All the talk about smallness again. He looked down at Prince standing in the mud among all the big English cockers. The rain had plastered Prince's fur close to his body so that he looked smaller than usual. Water dripped from his ears and ran off his back in little rivers. "Oh, Princey," Tom thought desperately, "it doesn't matter how small you are, but, please, have a sense of smell."

Prince was matched with a black English cocker in the first land series. As the dogs started off, each after a pheasant of his own, Tom studied Prince closely. Prince had his nose to the ground as usual. He was covering the field, first to the left and then to the right, just as he always did. But perhaps this was habit, Tom thought. Perhaps Prince wasn't smelling; perhaps he was only following a routine. Then Prince stopped in his tracks. He pushed his nose into the soggy grass and raised the little hump of his ears, the way he did when he was on the trail of a bird.

Tom grinned. Prince hadn't lost his sense of smell. Maybe everything would be all right, after all.

For a moment it did look as if everything would be all right. Prince found his bird, flushed it out of a bush, and slammed himself into a sitting position as the gun went off. Now he had to wait. This was always the

110

hardest part of hunting for Prince. Just when he wanted to go streaking across the fields, he had to sit down and wait for permission to go. But he never had long to wait, except sometimes in a trial, when his retrieve might interfere with the work of the other dog, he had to wait a little longer.

That was what happened now. Just as Prince would normally have been sent to retrieve, the black cocker flushed a pheasant right in front of Prince. And Prince wasn't supposed to move. He had to sit still, no matter how wriggly he felt, and watch the black cocker look for his bird. Prince wasn't even supposed to talk to the black cocker about it. He couldn't tell the black cocker he was looking in the wrong places. He couldn't make any comment when he saw the black cocker bump into a tree, become confused and start off in the wrong direction. No, Prince was expected to hold steady no matter what. He mustn't move even when the black cocker accidentally flushed another bird behind Prince.

There was a bird in front of Prince and a bird behind him! Prince could hear the bird behind him; he could see the bird in front flapping in the tall grass. Yet Prince didn't move. For more than five minutes, while his heart beat inside him like a drum, Prince sat as stony still as if his picture were being taken. He had to sit still for so long and through so many distractions that Tom began to wonder if, when the time came to retrieve, Prince would even remember where his bird had fallen.

At last the black cocker finished his work. At last the judge nodded to Tom. At last Tom raised his arm for Prince to go.

As if he had been shot out of a gun, Prince hurled himself across the field directly to his bird. He disappeared for a moment while he crouched down in a clump of grass. Then he stood up, and the bird was in his mouth. It was an unusually big bird—so big that the men could hardly see Prince behind the feathers. As he walked back across the fields, his eyes barely showing over the top of the big pheasant, Prince looked smaller than ever. But this time no one talked about his size. The owners of the English cockers looked at Prince with new respect.

"He showed fine control," they admitted grudgingly. "At least this time."

Again and again Prince showed the same kind of control and the same kind of spirit. So did many of the English cockers. At the end of the day no one really knew who was ahead. There was one thing, though, everyone did agree on. Prince Tom was one of the three leading dogs. He had a chance of winning first place the next day when the final series of the trial was to be run off.

16

RIGHT UP to the last event, on the second day of the field trial, no one of the three leading dogs was clearly ahead.

"It all depends on how they do in the water," people said as they gathered beside a small lake, waiting for the water trial to begin.

Tom's knees felt queer and slippery. Prince might win, he thought dizzily. He might actually win. If he did well in the water, Prince might become National Field Trial Champion.

Tom sat down on a rock. No one else seemed to be feeling the way he was, he noticed. The men with Tyrolean hats were walking their English cockers up and down and talking to them briskly. Tom looked more closely. Under their Tyrolean hats, the men did look worried. He could hear them telling each other how cold it was. "They're afraid, too," Tom thought. "They're afraid their dogs won't go into the water."

Well, that wasn't what Tom was afraid of. He just hoped Prince wouldn't go into the water too soon.

Prince was the only one at the edge of the lake who didn't seem to be afraid of anything. All the English cockers were shivering and looking longingly at the cars parked behind them. All the men with Tyrolean hats were looking sternly at the lake.

Then the first shot was fired and a bird dropped. The first English cocker was told to hold steady. He was delighted to hold steady. He hugged his tail close to the ground; he dug his feet in. He fixed his eyes on a distant spot across the lake and looked as if he would be willing to hold steady forever. When the order came to retrieve, the English cocker pretended he didn't understand. He clamped himself so firmly on the ground that he looked cemented to it. Finally, when he couldn't pretend any longer, the English cocker got up slowly and paddled unhappily into the water. He made his retrieve, but the whole idea was a lot of foolishness, he seemed to say as he pulled himself drooping and dripping out of the water.

All the English spaniels seemed to have the same opinion. Prince, standing on the side lines, could hardly choke back his up-and-down comments. His eyes snapped, his tail wriggled impatiently as one spaniel after another hesitated to go into the water on the first command. If Prince had been a boy instead of a dog, he would surely have let loose a long string

115

of words to show how he felt. As it was, all Prince could do was sit close to the water and wait his turn. He kept his hind legs and tail well off the ground, however, so that when the time came, he could make a fast take-off.

Prince made Tom think of an airplane warming up its motors. All four of Prince's motors were humming, Tom thought. Prince raised his tail another inch off the ground. Now the motors were racing and the propellers were beginning to turn. "Stay on the ground," Tom whispered. "Don't take off yet. Steady now."

Then it was Prince's turn. The gun was fired and the bird was dropped on the water. Tom kept one eye on the judge for his signal to let Prince go. He kept his other eye on Prince. "Keep the brakes on," Tom said to himself, hoping that somehow Prince would know what he was thinking. Tom's legs ached as though he, too, were struggling to hold down invisible brakes.

Out of one corner of his eye Tom saw Prince raise his tail another quarter of an inch, and just as he thought he couldn't keep Prince grounded a moment longer, the judge nodded. Tom raised his arm and, with one great spring, Prince took off into the air as if he really did have wings and engines and propellers. As he hit the water fifteen feet away from the shore, a great shout went up beside the lake. All the spec-

tators grinned and thumped each other on the back.

"That did it," the people said. "That will give Prince the championship for sure."

The people crowded around Tom and congratulated him. They said they had never seen a dog with as much spirit as Prince. Such a small dog, too. An American dog.

Tom felt a warm, tingling glow as if his own motors were humming. He wasn't at all sure he could hold himself steady through such a proud moment.

Perhaps the moment of victory at the lake was even better than the moment in the hunting lodge when the judges officially announced their decision, although the announcement was splendid. The room was quiet and the judge's voice sounded as if he might be crowning a king. Tom could almost hear trumpets blowing.

"The National Field Trial Champion for 1956," the judge said, "is Prince Tom III, owned by Tom Clute of Adrian, Michigan."

The judge handed Tom a silver cup almost as tall as Prince Tom.

Perhaps the best time of all came after the ceremony in the lodge. Tom went out to the car with the big cup to tell Prince the official news. Dogs weren't allowed in the hunting lodge. Tom put his arm around Prince and scratched the special place on his neck.

"Hi-ya, Champ," Tom said.

Suddenly Tom felt something strange on Prince's neck. A piece of metal seemed to be attached to Prince's collar. Tom pushed aside the fur to look and found a little silver horseshoe dangling from the collar.

Tom smiled. He knew that horseshoe. He knew it always lay in the bottom of Nathan's pocket. He had often seen Nathan take the horseshoe and rub it between his fingers.

"Maybe this really helped," Tom said. Holding the horseshoe between his fingers, he felt that Michigan wasn't so far away, after all. He almost felt as if Nathan had been at the trial too. "I bet we wouldn't even be here today if it weren't for Nathan," Tom said.

He scratched Prince thoughtfully. "You know what we're going to do, Princey?" he said. "We're going to take Nathan back a present. And we're going to get it right now."

Tom turned the key to start the black and white station wagon and he headed for the nearest New Jersey town. Slowly he drove up and down the main street, looking for a special kind of store. At last he found what he was looking for—a printing shop with all kinds of lettering and sample signs in the window. Tom parked the car and he and Prince went inside the store.

"I want a long strip of your best cardboard," Tom said to the owner of the printing shop. "A strip about four feet long. I'd like to have you print on the cardboard in the very best printing you can do." Tom thought for a moment. "Perhaps the cardboard should be red," he added. "And the letters should be black and gold. I want the sign to be very special-looking."

Tom took a pencil and a piece of paper out of his pocket. He wrote some letters and handed the paper to the owner of the shop. "This is what I want you to print on the cardboard," Tom said.

PRINCE TOM III, C.D., C.D.X., U.D., N.F.T.C.

Tom looked down at Prince. "That's a pretty long name," he said. "I don't see how it could be any longer. I don't see how you could have any more ideas."

Prince's eyes sparkled. He wagged his tail back and forth in his old try-me way.

Tom chuckled. "Oh, I suppose you'll think of something," he said. He ruffled the fur on the top of Prince's head. "You little rascal."

PRINCE TOM III, C.D. U.D., N.F.T.C.

Champion **Prince Tom** among his trophies